Jesus
and his
Friends

Leena Lane – Gillian Chapman

Jesus chooses his first disciples

One day Jesus was speaking to crowds of people on the shore of Lake Galilee.

Jesus stepped into a boat belonging to Simon and spoke from the boat.

When he had finished speaking, Jesus asked Simon to row the boat out into the deeper water and let down the nets.

'We've worked hard all night,' said Simon, 'and haven't caught a single sardine. But if you tell me, I'll do it.'

So off they went – and their nets were filled to overflowing with fish!

Simon was amazed. He knew there was something very special about Jesus. James and John, Simon's partners, couldn't believe their eyes either.

'Don't be afraid,' said Jesus. 'Follow me. I will make you fishers of people.'

So the fishermen left their nets and followed Jesus.

Luke 5, verses 1 to 11

Something to think about:
Jesus asked the fishermen to follow him and they did so.

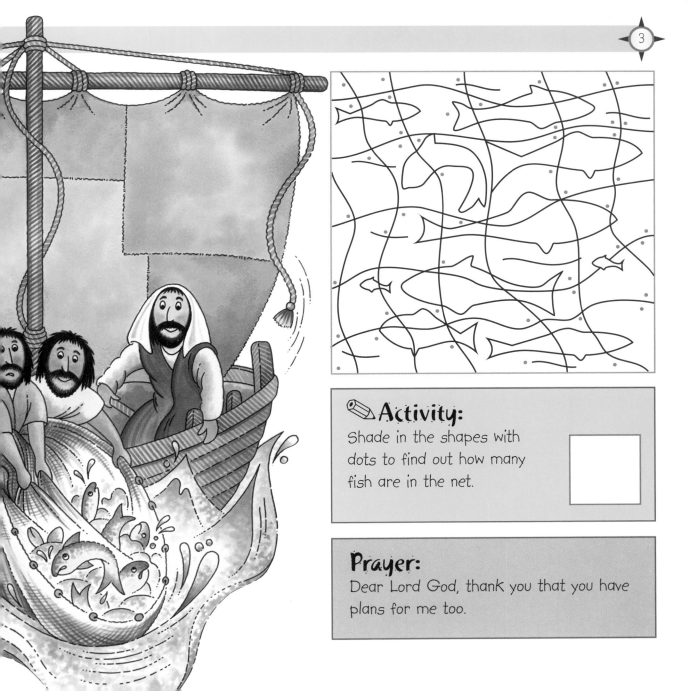

✏️ Activity:

Shade in the shapes with dots to find out how many fish are in the net.

Prayer:

Dear Lord God, thank you that you have plans for me too.

Jesus chooses a tax collector

Jesus saw a tax collector called Matthew, sitting at the place where Jews paid taxes to the Romans.

Everyone hated the tax collectors.

Jesus spoke to Matthew. 'Come and follow me!' he said.

At once Matthew left everything and went away with Jesus.

He held a big meal at his home for Jesus. He invited other tax collectors and guests.

Some teachers of the Law muttered to each other. Then they spoke to Jesus' disciples.

'Why do you eat and drink with those people?' they asked.

Jesus heard them and answered, 'I came to invite them to know God.' he said. 'They need to know how much God loves them, just like everyone else.'

Matthew 9, verses 9 to 13

Something to think about:

Jesus especially welcomed people who were hated by other people.

✎ Activity:

How many coins are there?

 **+** [ ] **=** [ ]

Prayer:
Dear God, help me to accept and love other people as Jesus did.

✎ Activity:
Can you design your own coin? Draw a face, picture or pattern in the blank coin above.

Jesus blesses the children

People loved to bring their children to Jesus for him to bless. Jesus welcomed them with open arms.

But Jesus' friends were not very happy about it. 'Don't bother him with the children,' they said to the mothers and fathers who brought their children to Jesus. 'Jesus is too busy.'

Jesus overheard them. Jesus was never too busy for children.

'Let the children come to me,' he said. 'Don't try to stop them. My Kingdom belongs to people who are like these children. You will never enter God's Kingdom if you don't enter it like a child.'

Luke 18, verses 15 to 17

Something to think about:

What did Jesus mean about God's Kingdom belonging to children?

Prayer:
Dear God, thank you that you love me and always have time for me.

✎ **Activity:**
Can you help this child to find his way through the maze to Jesus?

Zacchaeus

Jesus was walking through Jericho. A man lived there called Zacchaeus. He was a very rich man and was in charge of collecting taxes in the area.

Zacchaeus was a very short man. He heard that Jesus was coming, but he wasn't tall enough to see over the heads of the crowd. So he climbed a tree to see Jesus.

Jesus called to him in the tree: 'Zacchaeus, come down! I want to come to your house today.'

Zacchaeus was very pleased to welcome Jesus to his house. But other people started complaining.

'Zacchaeus is a bad man! Why does Jesus want to eat with him?' they asked.

Zacchaeus later told the crowds of people that he was going to change for the better:

'I want to give half of all I own to the poor. If I have cheated anyone, I will pay them back four times as much.'

Luke 19, verses 1 to 10

Something to think about:

Zacchaeus wanted to change when he met Jesus. He became a generous man.

Prayer:

Dear God, thank you that you are interested in everyone, even when other people have no time for them.

Activity:

Can you spot ten differences between the two pictures?

A gift for Jesus

While Jesus was in Bethany he had dinner with a man named Simon.

A woman came into the room with a very expensive bottle of perfume. She poured it on Jesus' head while he sat at the table. The smell of the perfume wafted through the whole house.

'Why waste all that money on that perfume?' someone muttered. 'It could have been sold for a high price, and the money could have been given to the poor!'

Jesus answered, 'Leave her alone! She has done a very special thing. You will always have the poor, but you won't always have me.'

Jesus knew that he was soon going to die.

Matthew 26, verses 6 to 13

 Activity:

Can you find three identical pairs of presents. Connect each pair with a line.

✎ Activity:

Can you colour the gift box below to look like the one above?

Now design and colour your own wrapping for the gift below.

Jesus brings Lazarus back to life

Jesus had a good friend called Lazarus, who lived in a town many miles away.

Jesus heard that Lazarus was ill. But by the time Jesus reached the town, Lazarus was dead.

Jesus wept. He had loved his friend. He went to the tomb where Lazarus' body had been put. It had been there for four days already. A large stone was rolled across the tomb.

Jesus told some men to roll the stone aside.

He prayed aloud to God. 'Thank you, Father, that you hear my prayers.'

Then Jesus shouted, 'Come out, Lazarus!'

Lazarus walked out into the daylight, still covered in his grave clothes, with a cloth over his face, but very much alive!

Many people watching now knew that Jesus had been sent from God. They began to see that they could trust him to help them.

John 11, verses 1 to 44

Something to think about:

Jesus understands about the things that make us sad. He cried when he found that his friend had died.

Prayer:

Dear God, thank you that Jesus showed us your amazing power, even to bring the dead back to life.

✎ Activity:

Can you find the eight picture fragments in the big picture?

Write the number of each fragment in the boxes provided.

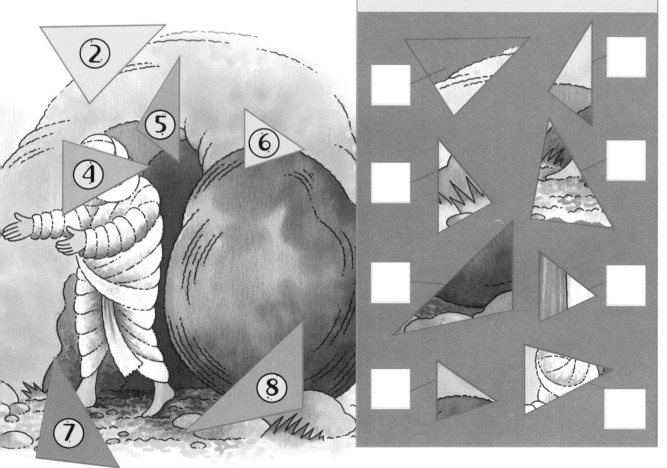

Jesus washes his friends' feet

Jesus met his twelve friends in the upper room of a house in Jerusalem. It was time for the Passover feast.

Jesus took a bowl of water and began to wash his friends' feet.

'Don't wash my feet!' said Peter. 'You're our master, not our servant!'

'Unless I wash you, you don't belong to me,' said Jesus.

Peter was astonished but his answer was quick:

'Then wash my hands and head as well!'

But Jesus said that only his feet needed washing. Peter let Jesus wash them.

'Now that I have washed your feet,' said Jesus, 'you must also wash each other's feet. Do as I have done.'

John 13, verses 1 to 15

Something to think about:

Jesus wants us to look after and help each other, not push ourselves forward as if we are more important than other people.

✎ Activity:

Which of the jug and bowl sets above did Jesus use in the big picture opposite?

✎ Activity:
There are three things wrong with this trail. Can you circle the three footprints that are odd?

Prayer:
Dear God, help me to be kind to other people. What can I do to help someone today?

Judas kisses Jesus

Jesus went to the Garden of Gethsemane to pray. He knew that the time was soon coming when he would be arrested. Jesus needed his friends with him. He asked them to pray with him, but they were tired, and they kept falling asleep.

Suddenly, Judas Iscariot appeared. Behind him there was a noisy crowd brandishing swords and clubs.

Judas stepped forward and kissed Jesus on the cheek. It was a sign that one friend would give to another. But it was also a sign to the guards that this man was Jesus. Judas had betrayed his friend. The guards seized Jesus and took him away.

Mark 14, verses 43 to 46

Something to think about:
Why do you think Judas turned against Jesus?

Prayer:
Dear God, please help me to be a good friend and not turn against you as Judas did.

✎ Activity:
Can you find the ten deliberate, crazy mistakes in the big picture? It should look like the picture below.

Peter's betrayal

Jesus was arrested in the Garden of Gethsemane and brought before a court of chief priests. They tried to find a reason for putting him to death. But Jesus had done nothing wrong.

Peter, one of Jesus' closest friends, waited outside in the courtyard to see what would happen next. He was very afraid.

A girl saw Peter and said, 'You were with Jesus, weren't you?'

'No!' said Peter. 'I don't know what you're talking about!'

The girl said to the people standing around, 'Look! He is one of Jesus' friends!'

'No I'm not!' said Peter.

Later, some other people recognised Peter and said, 'You know Jesus!'

Again, Peter said he did not know Jesus.

Then he heard a cockerel crow twice. He remembered something Jesus had said to him: 'Before a cockerel crows twice, you will say three times that you do not know me at all.'

Peter wept. He had betrayed his friend Jesus.

Mark 14, verses 66 to 72

Something to think about:

Would you stand up for Jesus if you were in Peter's place?

✎ Activity:

How many times did the cockerel crow? Join the red dots with just six lines to find out.

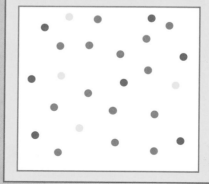

✏️ Activity:

Which of the six smaller cockerels is the same as the large one?

1

2

3

4

5

6

Prayer: Dear God, help me to stand up for you, even when people tease me or say bad things.

Jesus cares for his mother

After Jesus' trial, he was taken away to be nailed to a cross. They crucified him, along with two thieves, on a hillside outside the city.

The soldiers who were watching took his clothes and shared them out among themselves, but they gambled for his robe which was made from one piece of cloth.

Jesus' mother, Mary, stood nearby, weeping. Her sister was there too, and two other women who were his friends. Jesus looked from the cross and saw his friend John in the crowd. He spoke to his mother.

'Dear mother, here is your son,' he said.

Then he spoke to John:

'Dear friend, here is your mother.'

So John took Jesus' mother away to look after her in his home, just as Jesus wanted.

John 19, verses 25 to 27

Prayer:
Please help me always to think of others before myself.

✎ Activity:

Colour in the picture of John comforting Mary.

Mary was very upset. Can you draw a sad face?

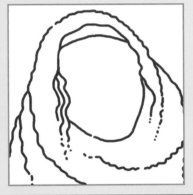

Something to think about:

Even when Jesus was in pain and dying, he thought of other people first.

Thomas believes

After Jesus had died, God raised him from death. The disciples all saw him – all except Thomas. Thomas did not believe Jesus could be alive again.

'Unless I see his hands and put my finger where the nails were hammered in, I shall not believe.'

A week later, Thomas and some of Jesus' friends were together. All the doors were locked. Suddenly Jesus appeared there with them!

'Peace be with you!' said Jesus. Then he turned to Thomas. 'Look at my hands. Put your finger in my wounds. Stop doubting and believe.'

Thomas said, 'My Lord and my God!' He worshipped Jesus.

'You have believed in me because you have seen me,' said Jesus. 'Happy are the people who believe even though they have not seen me.'

John 20, verses 24 to 29

Something to think about:

What would you say to someone who can't believe Jesus is alive because they haven't seen him?

Prayer:

Dear God, thank you for helping us to believe Jesus is alive, even though we haven't seen him.

✎ Activity:

Can you fill in the missing letters?

| J | | S | | | is | | | i | v | |

✎ Activity:

Can you find the following ten words?

- ☐ JESUS
- ☐ DISCIPLES
- ☐ THOMAS
- ☐ HANDS
- ☐ DOUBT
- ☐ WOUNDS
- ☐ BELIEF
- ☐ FAITH
- ☐ PEACE
- ☐ HAPPY

```
G J E S U S
D P E H R C
R O H A E O
E Z A P B E
Q T D I S C I P L E S
W H A N D S F P P L W
A O R D N Y S Y E I O
R M W O U N D S A E U
B A I U J J F W C F N
Y S T B R H Y N E O D
F A I T H Y M D S T S
```

Published in the UK by
The Bible Reading Fellowship
First Floor, Elsfield Hall, 15-17 Elsfield Way, Oxford OX2 8FG
ISBN 1 84101 407 9

First edition 2004

Editorial Director Annette Reynolds
Art Director Gerald Rogers
Pre-production Krystyna Hewitt
Production John Laister

British Library Cataloguing in Publication Data.
A catalogue record for this book is available from the
British Library.

Printed and bound in Singapore